Lets Explore the Languages of Africa!
Yoruba Alphabet Coloring Book©

By Ayobooks™

ISBN: 061556318X

ISBN-13: 978-0-615-56318-3

This Book Belongs To

_____

A

Sounds like Ahh

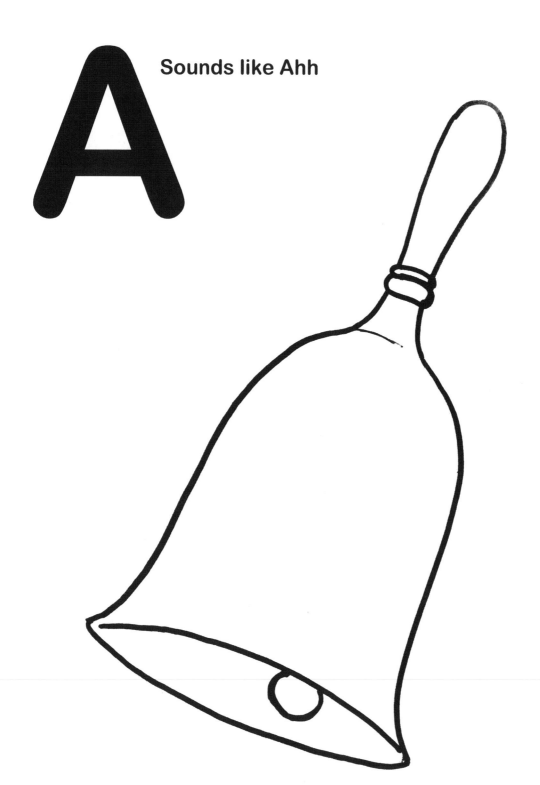

Agogo: Bell

Sounds like Bee

B

Bùbá: Shirt

D Sounds like Dee

Dígí: Mirror

Sounds like Ay

Etí: Ear

E

Sounds like Eh

Ẹja: Fish

Sounds like Fee

F

Fìlà: Hat

G

Sounds like Gee

Gèlè: Headtie

Sounds like Gbi!

GB

Gbó: Old

H

Sounds like Hee

Hù: To Grow

Sounds like Eee

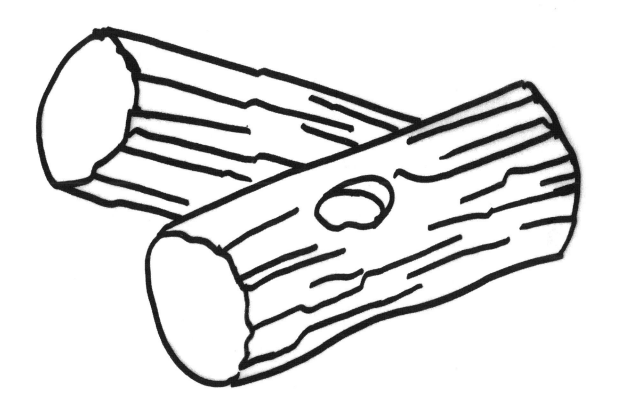

Igi: Wood

J

Sounds like Jee

Jigi: Eyeglasses

Sounds like Kee

K

Kìnìún: Lion

L

Sounds like Lee

Labalábá: Butterfly

Sounds like Mee M

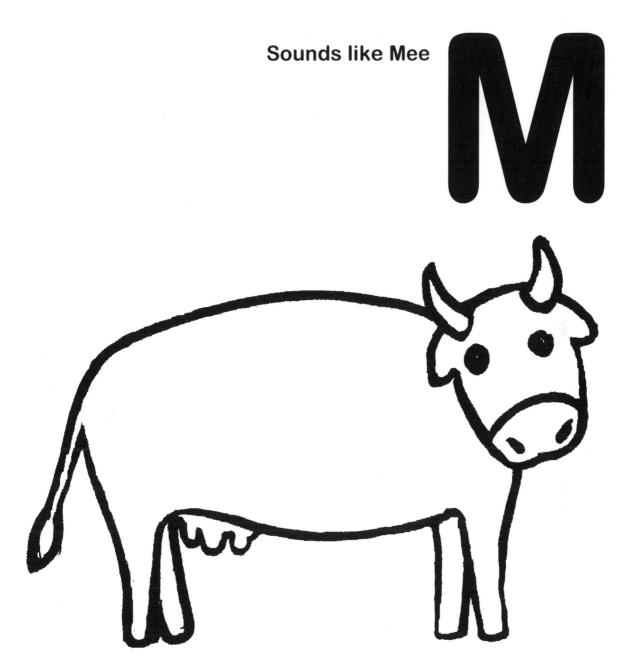

Màlúù: Cow

N

Sounds like Nee

Ekáàbò!
(Welcome)

Ní: To Say

Sounds like Oh

O

Otútù: Cold

Ọ

Sounds like Or

Ọmọrí-odó: Pestle

Sounds like kpee

P

Pòn: To Carry

R

Ribiti: Round

S

Sùn: Sleep

Ṣ

Sounds like She

Ṣíbi: Spoon

T

Tìmtìm: Cushion

Sounds like Oo

isu̱: Yam

26

Sounds like Wee

W

Wàrà: Milk

Y

Sounds like Yee

Yín: To Lay Eggs

A	**B**	**D**	**E**	**Ẹ**
(Ah)	(Bee)	(Dee)	(Ay)	(Eh)
F	**G**	**GB**	**H**	**I**
(Fee)	(Gee)	(Gbi!)	(Hee)	(Ee)
J	**K**	**L**	**M**	**N**
(Jee)	(Kee)	(Lee)	(Mee)	(Nee)
O	**Ọ**	**P**	**R**	**S**
(Oh)	(Or)	(Kpee)	(Ree)	(See)
Ṣ	**T**	**U**	**W**	**Y**
(She)	(Tee)	(Oo)	(Wee)	(Yee)

1	Èní	6	Ẹ̀fà
2	Èjì	7	Èje
3	Ẹ̀ta	8	Ẹ̀jọ
4	Ẹ̀rin	9	Èsán
5	Àrùn	10	Ẹ̀wá

Made in the USA
San Bernardino, CA
25 September 2018